---

1. Write out each number in words.

1   **one**   2 ....   3 ....

4 ....   5 ....   6 ....

14 ....   15 ....   16 ....

---

2. Read these numbers out loud.

7   8   9   10   11   12   13

17   18   19   20

---

3. Start at twenty and write all the numbers in order down to nine. Some have been done for you.

| | 19 | | | 16 | |

| 14 | | | 11 | | |

Number and Place Value

1. How many shapes are there in each group?

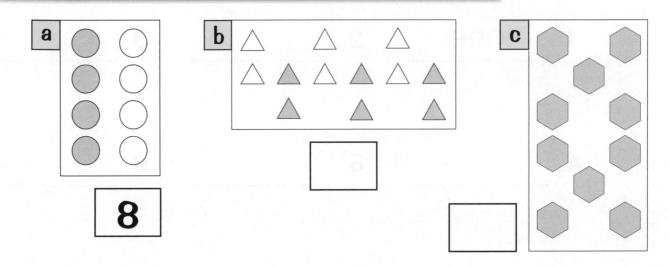

a `8`

b

c

2. Count how many arrows there are. Write your answers in words.

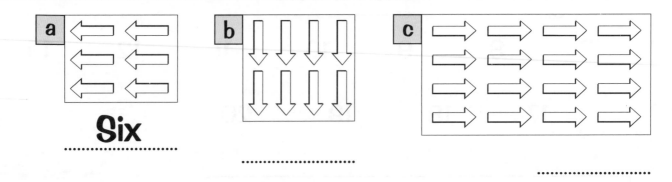

a Six

b

c

3. How many of each fruit are there?

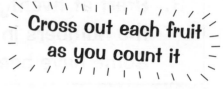
Cross out each fruit as you count it

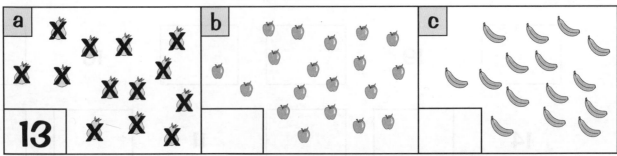

a `13`

b

c

Number and Place Value

1. Write 15 in the right place on this number line.

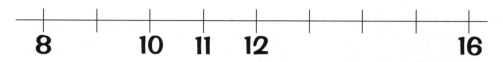

8   10 11 12   16

2. Circle all the even numbers.

8   15   4   9   30

Even numbers end in a 0, 2, 4, 6 or 8

23   22   11   25

3. Colour in the smallest odd number.

Odd numbers end in a 1, 3, 5, 7 or 9

20   13   42

35   6   11   17

Number and Place Value

1. What numbers are shown below?

a 14

b

c

Count the tens and ones

2. Put the right number in each box.

a **16** = 10 and 6

b 11 = [ ] and 1

c 14 = 10 and [ ]

d 18 = [ ] and 8

3. Write the next two numbers in each list.

a 5 6 7 **8** **9**

b 46 45 44 [ ] [ ]

c 97 98 99 [ ] [ ]

d 104 103 102 [ ] [ ]

Number and Place Value

---

1. How many fish and chips are there in the picture below?

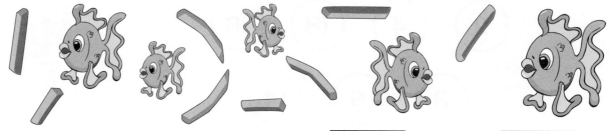

There are ⬜ fish and ⬜ chips.

---

2. Circle the correct word below.

There are ⬜ more / fewer ⬜ fish than chips in Question 1.

---

3. Circle the ladybird with the least spots.

---

4. Tick the two sets that have an equal number of cubes.

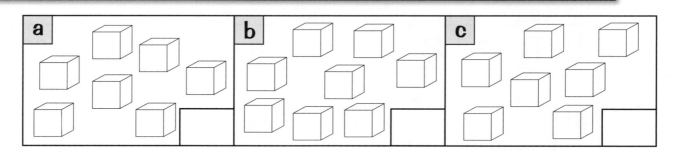

 **Ordering Numbers**

---

1. Join up the numbers by counting up in twos.

(2)—(4) (18) (16)

(8) (6) (14)

(10) (12)

---

2. Count on 5 from each of these numbers.
Write which number you stop at.

a 0 **5** .... **b** 5 .... **c** 13 .... **d** 16 ....

---

3. Count back 10 from each of these numbers.
Write which number you stop at.

a 14 **4** .... **b** 18 .... **c** 32 .... **d** 57 ....

---

4. Give the numbers that are 1 less
and 1 more than these numbers.

	1 less		1 more			1 less		1 more			1 less		1 more
a	6	7	8		**b**		13			**c**		20	
d		23			**e**		24			**f**		29	

Ordering Numbers

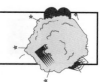

---

1. For each pair of numbers, write the number which is less than the other.

a	5, 7	**5**
b	12, 9	....
c	14, 19	....

d	18, 5	....
e	19, 21	....
f	30, 13	....

---

2. For each pair of numbers, write the number which is more than the other.

a	17, 13	....
b	21, 12	....
c	18, 28	....

---

3. Write these numbers in order with the smallest first.

9   7   18   3̶   11   16   13   5

| **3** | | | | | | | |

---

4. Write these numbers in order with the largest first.

10   19   12   15   2   6   2̶0̶   8

| **20** | | | | | | | |

312   *Ordering Numbers*

1. Match each mouse to the place it comes in the race.

2nd   3rd   1st   4th

2. Look at the bears below. The 1st bear is wearing a bow tie.

Circle the 3rd bear.

Which bear has a hat on?

Write your answer as 1st, 2nd, 3rd 4th or 5th. ....

3. Draw two more shapes to carry on the pattern.

....

Adding

1. Write the totals.

a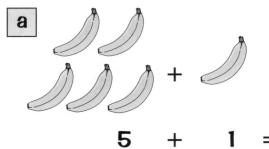

5 + 1 = ...

b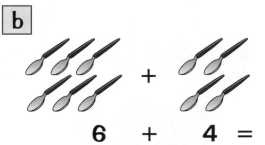

6 + 4 = ...

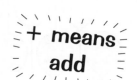

+ means add

2. Work out the answers below.

a 3 + 4 = **7**

b 5 + 4 = ...

c 6 + 0 = ...

d 4 + 4 = ...

e 5 + 3 = ...

f 7 + 2 = ...

3. Make different pairs of numbers that add up to 7.

| 0 | + | 7 | = | 7 |

| | + | | = | 7 |

| | + | | = | 7 |

| | + | | = | 7 |

Adding

1. Fill in the missing + and = signs.

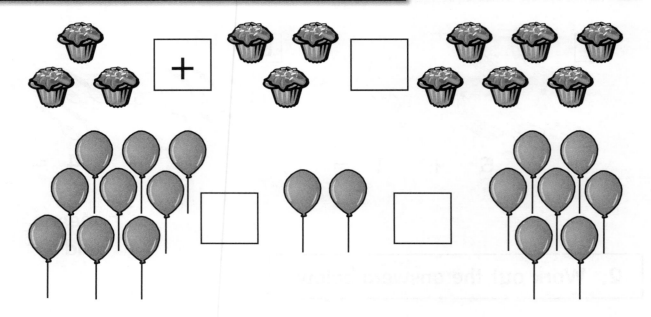

2. Circle the pairs of numbers that make 20.

(5 + 15)   3 + 14   16 + 5

10 + 10   8 + 12

0 + 10   11 + 7   13 + 17

3. Work out 16 + 7 using the number line. Show the steps and circle your answer.

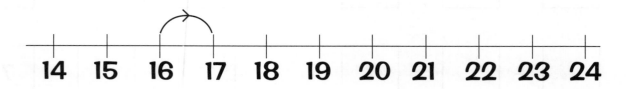

Adding

---

1. Fill in each gap with a + or = sign.

a 8 $=$ 6 + 2

b 3 ☐ 6 = 9

c 7 ☐ 0 = 7

d 11 ☐ 7 + 4

e 7 ☐ 6 + 1

f 7 ☐ 6 = 13

---

2. Work out these answers.

a Add 2 and 4   **6**

b The total of five and 2 ....

c Put together 6 and 1 ....

d Seven add seven ....

e Five add zero ....

f The total of six and 8 ....

---

3. Find the total of each pair of numbers.

a 11, 6   **17** ....

b 7, 12 ....

c 13, 5 ....

d 14, 3 ....

e 10, 8 ....

f 2, 15 ....

Subtracting

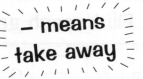

1. Fill in the answers.

– means take away

$5 - 3 =$ ....

$8 - 2 =$ ....

2. Find the difference between the numbers of cats and dogs.

3. Work out the answers below.

| a | $6 - 3 =$ **3** | b | $7 - 4 =$ .... | c | $8 - 3 =$ .... |

| d | $15 - 4 =$ .... | e | $17 - 6 =$ .... |

| f | $19 - 5 =$ .... | g | $16 - 3 =$ .... |

Subtracting

---

1. **Fill in the missing numbers.**

a 14 – 4 = **10**   b [ ] – 5 = 11

c 17 – [ ] = 17   d 13 – 6 = [ ]

---

2. **Subtract the smaller number from the larger number.**

a 7, 19 **12**   b 18, 6 ....

c 3, 18 ....   d 13, 2 ....

e 16, 4 ....   f 17, 3 ....

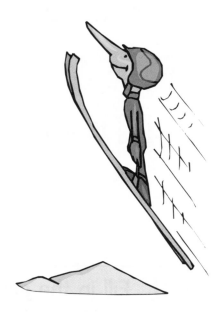

---

3. **Work out these answers.**

a 7 take away 0   **7** ....   b Subtract 3 from 9 ....

c The difference
   between 2 and 5 ....   d Take away 8 from ten ....

e The distance
   between 4 and six ....   f Take away 4 from 8 ....

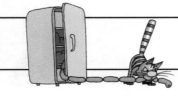

Subtracting

---

1. **Finish the number sentences below.**

a If ten minus four = 6, then 10 – 6 equals   **4** ....

b If 9 take away 4 = 5, then nine minus five equals ....

c If 8 minus 6 = two, then 8 – 2 equals ....

---

2. **Circle the answers on the number lines.**

a 10 – 2

2   3   4   5   6   7   8   9   10

b 16 – 5

11   12   13   14   15   16   17   18   19   20

---

3. Fill in the gaps using numbers smaller than ten.

a 8 – 5 = 3   **b** ☐ – ☐ = 5

c ☐ – ☐ = 4   **d** ☐ – ☐ = 2

e ☐ – ☐ = 6   **f** ☐ – ☐ = 1

Multiplying

---

1. Complete these sets of food items to show double the amount.

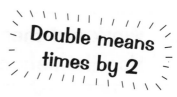

Double means times by 2

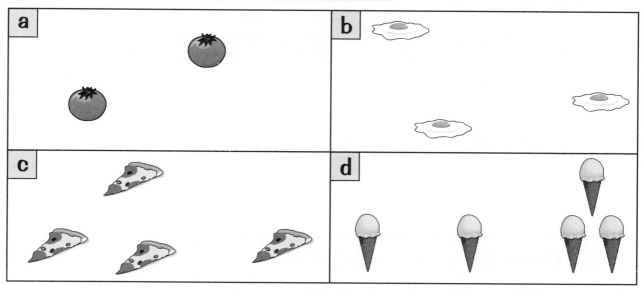

a

b

c

d

---

2. Fill in the missing numbers to find the total number of cherries.

× means times by

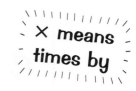

$3 \times 3 = \boxed{}$

$5 \times \boxed{} = \boxed{}$

---

3. Show 4 × 2 on the number line. Circle the number you end on.

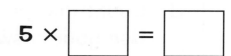 

0   1   2   3   4   5   6   7   8   9   10

Multiplying

1. **Work out these answers.**
   Use the sets of pencils to help you.

   a **4 × 3 =**  = ...

   b **3 × 4 =** = ...

2. **Circle the sum that has the**
   same answer as the large number.

   a **4** | 2 × 2 |
                  | 3 × 2 |

   b **14** | 9 × 2 |
                   | 7 × 2 |

   c **16** | 8 × 2 |
                   | 6 × 2 |

3. **Count the groups in two different ways.**
   Use your answers to fill in the missing numbers.

   [ ] groups of 2

   [ ] groups of 3

   [ ] × [ ] = 6

Multiplying

1. Draw the answer to each sum and then write the correct answer in the box. The first one is done for you.

| a | 3 × 2 | | = | **6** |

b | 5 × 1 | = | |

c | 2 × 5 | = | |

d | 4 × 2 | = | |

2. Match the multiplications with the right answers.

  3 × 5   4

 2 × 6   15

4 × 1   10

5 × 2   12

Dividing

---

1. **Share the bones between the two dogs equally.**

Each dog has ☐ bones.

---

2. **Answer these questions.**
Use the groups of caps to help you.

a How many 3s in 6?

☐

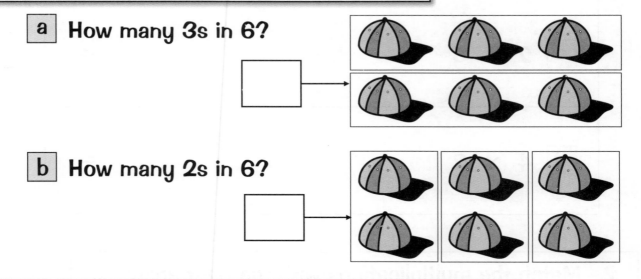

b How many 2s in 6?

☐

---

3. **Share these books into four groups of three.**
Fill in the missing numbers.

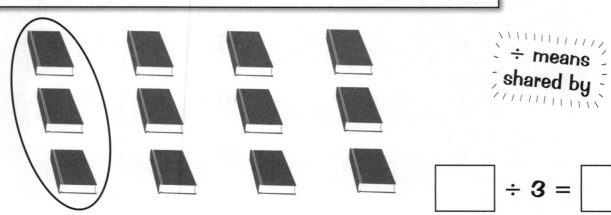

÷ means
shared by

☐ ÷ 3 = ☐

Dividing

---

1. How many groups of 4 carrots are there below?

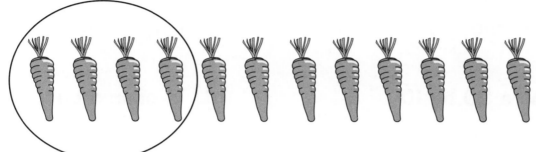

....

---

2. How many groups of 2 are in 10?
Use the number line to help you.

| | | | | | | | | | | |
|0|1|2|3|4|5|6|7|8|9|10|

There are ☐ groups of 2 in 10.

---

3. Use the number lines to fill in the divisions below.

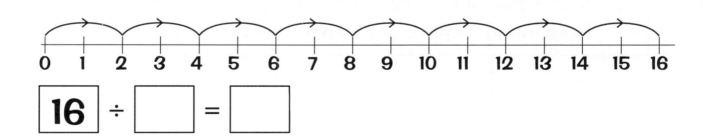

16 ÷ ☐ = ☐

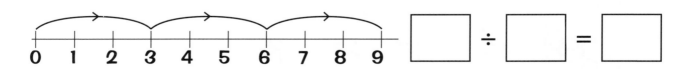

☐ ÷ ☐ = ☐

Dividing

---

1. **Work out the answers below.**

a 2 ÷ two   **1** ....

b Fifty ÷ ten ....

c Share 30 by 10 ....

d 14 shared by 2 ....

---

2. Join the sums in the balloons to the correct answers on the sheep. One has been done for you.

---

3. Share the sweets below between three people. How many sweets does each person get?

.... sweets

Fractions

---

1. Colour in half of each square.
The first one has been done for you.

A half is one of two equal parts

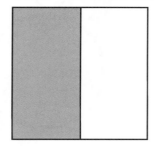 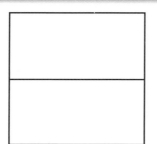 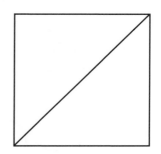

---

2. Cross out half of each set of objects.
The first set has been done for you.

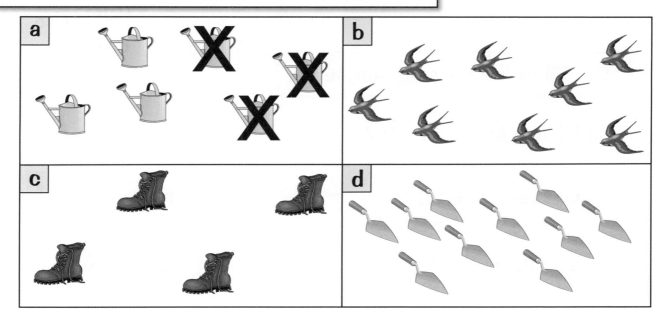

a

b

c

d

---

3. Write half of each number.

a 12 **6** ....

b twenty ....

c eight ....

d 14 ....

e 16 ....

f 60 ....

Fractions

---

1. Colour in half the circles in each row.
The first one has been done for you.

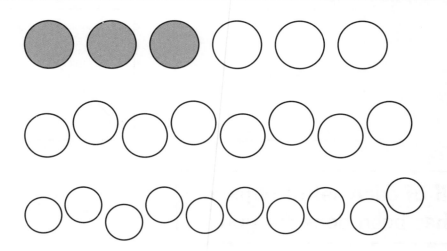

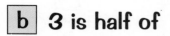

Half is also
written $\frac{1}{2}$

---

2. Fill in the missing numbers.

a five is half of **10** ....

b 3 is half of ....

c one is half of ....

d seven is $\frac{1}{2}$ of ....

e four is $\frac{1}{2}$ of ....

f 8 is half of ....

---

3. Draw the other half of each shape.
The first one has been done for you.

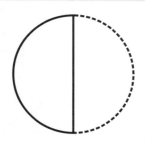

Fractions

1. Colour in a quarter of each shape.
The first one has been done for you.

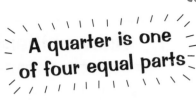

A quarter is one of four equal parts

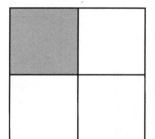 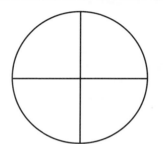 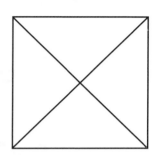

2. Circle a quarter of these eggs.

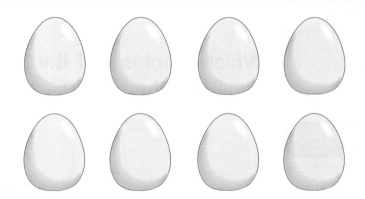

One quarter is also written $\frac{1}{4}$

3. How much of each shape is shaded?
Choose from these options.

$\frac{1}{4}$ $\frac{1}{2}$

one whole

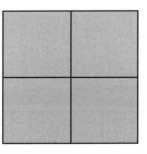 **a**

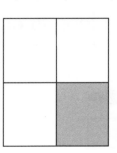 **b**

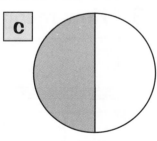 **c**

Measuring Problems

---

1. Answer these questions by putting 'A' or 'B' in each box.

 **Which van is longer?**

A

B

b Which hat is shorter?

A   B

---

2. Tick the right boxes below.

Which bat is double the length of the other?

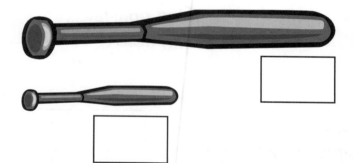

Which stool is half the height of the other?

---

3. How many blocks long is each pen?

A

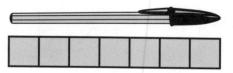

B

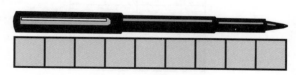

Pen A = [   ] blocks long   Pen B = [   ] blocks long

Measuring Problems

---

1. How long is this toothbrush?

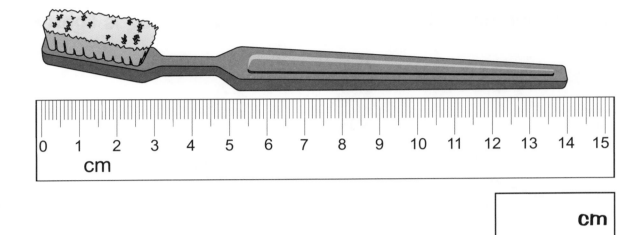

	cm

---

2. Draw a car that is 12 cm long.

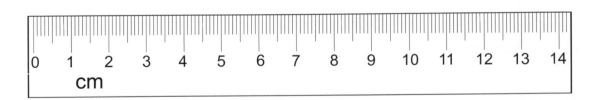

---

3. Draw a tree that is 3 cm tall.

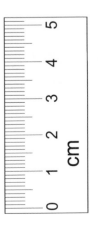

Measuring Problems

1. **Answer these questions by putting 'A' or 'B' in the boxes.**

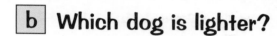

| a Which cat is heavier? | b Which dog is lighter? |

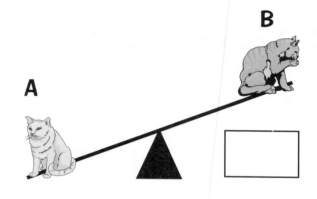
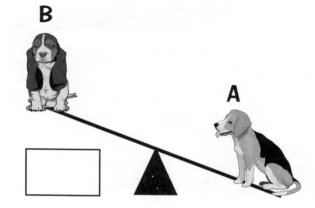

2. **How much does this block weigh?**

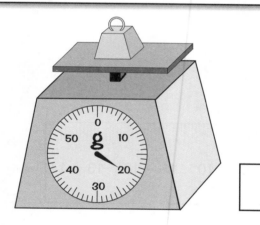

You can weigh things in grams

g

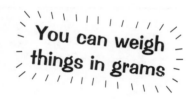

3. **An orange weighs 40 g.**
   Draw this on the scales.

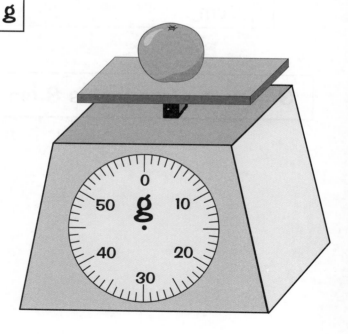

Measuring Problems

---

1.   Tick the right box below for each pair.

| Less than half full | More than a quarter full |

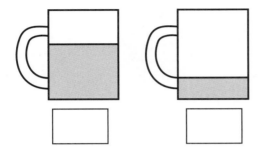

---

2.   Which watering can holds less liquid?   Tick the right box.

 5 cups fill this watering can.

 7 cups fill this watering can.

3.   How much water do these measuring jugs contain?

Volume can be measured in litres (l)

l

l

l

Money Problems

1. Match the values to the coins.

| 2p | 50p | £1 | 20p | 10p |

2. Circle the coin with the highest value.
   Put a cross through the coin with the lowest value.

3. Which note is worth the most? Tick the right box.

☐   ☐   ☐

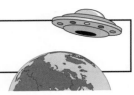

Time Problems

---

1. Write the days of the week in order.

Tuesday ....

Friday ....

---

2. Fill in the gaps.

a) If today is Monday, tomorrow will be **Tuesday** ....

b) If today is Friday, yesterday was ....

c) The month straight after June is ....

d) The month just before April is ....

e) There are .... months in a year.

---

3. Circle the part of the day that comes first.
Cross out the part of the day that comes last.

Evening   Morning   Afternoon

Time Problems

---

1. Write down the times shown on each clock.

a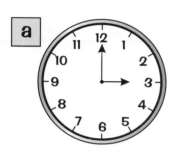

3 o'clock

b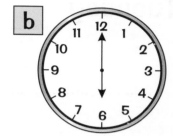

c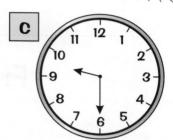

---

2. Draw hands on the clock faces to show the right times.

Eleven o'clock

Half past twelve

---

3. What time is shown on these digital clocks?

 **4 o'clock**

Time Problems

---

1.   Circle the quicker time for each pair.

a

15 seconds   51 seconds

b

3 minutes   23 minutes

---

2.   Use the words 'quicker' or 'slower' to fill in the gaps.

a **3 minutes is** .... **than 1 minute.**

b **7 hours is** .... **than 9 hours.**

c **15 seconds is** .... **than 40 seconds.**

---

3.   Circle the clocks that show a time later than 4 o'clock.

Shape

1. Join each shape to its name using a pencil line.

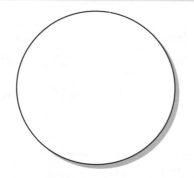

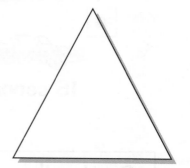

square   triangle   circle

2. Put a tick (✓) in all of the rectangles below.

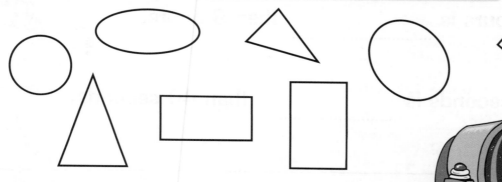

3. Draw a picture using squares, circles, triangles and rectangles.

Shape

1. Colour in all of the triangles below.

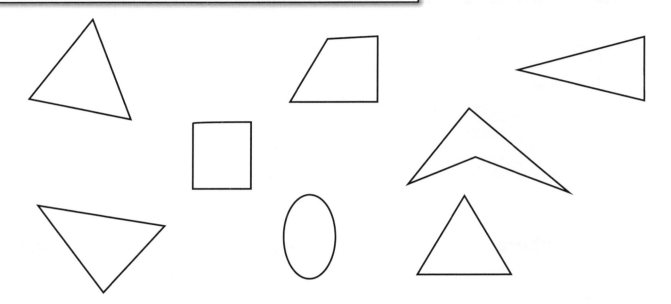

2. Draw a rectangle in the box below.

3. Colour the odd one out red and the other shapes blue.

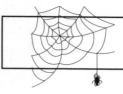

Shape

---

1. Join each shape to its name.

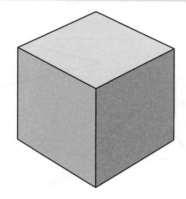 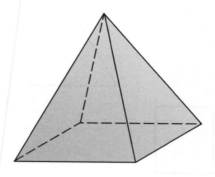 

sphere   cube   pyramid

---

2. Colour the sphere in red. Colour the cube in blue.

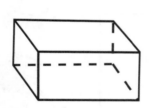 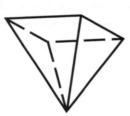  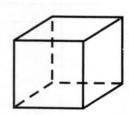

---

3. Circle each cuboid.

Position and Direction

---

1. Fill in the gaps with the correct words.
Choose the words from these options.

left
right
between

The knife is _____ the fork and spoon.

The fork is to the _____ of the knife.

The spoon is to the _____ of the knife.

---

2. Circle the right words.

The computer is

on top of / underneath

the desk.

The books are

on top of / underneath

the desk.

---

3. Which direction is the mouse moving in?
Tick the right box.

Up [ ]   Backwards [ ]

Down [ ]   Forwards [ ]

Position and Direction

1. An arrow starts by pointing up. Draw the arrow after it makes a quarter turn anticlockwise.

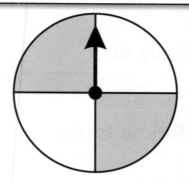

2. The clock hand starts at 6. It turns until it finishes on 3. Tick the correct turn made by the hand.

Quarter turn clockwise

Half turn

Three-quarter turn clockwise

Start

Finish

3. The clock hand starts at 3. What number is it pointing to after it has made a half turn?

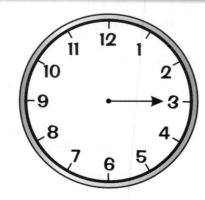

....

Answers — Pages 1 to 11

PAGE 1

Q1. (one) two three
four five six
fourteen fifteen sixteen
Q2. Numbers 7-13 and 17-20
should be read out loud.
Q3. 20, (19), 18, 17, (16), 15,
(14), 13, 12, (11), 10, 9

PAGE 2

Q1. a) (8)
b) 12
c) 10
Q2. a) (Six)
b) Eight
c) Sixteen
Q3. a) (13)
b) 19
c) 15

PAGE 3

Q1.

8   10 11 12   15 16
Q2. 8, 4, 30 and 22 should be circled.
Q3. 11 should be coloured in.

PAGE 4

Q1. a) (14)
b) 22
c) 30
Q2. a) (16)
b) 10
c) 4
d) 10
Q3. a) (8), (9)
b) 43, 42
c) 100, 101
d) 101, 100

PAGE 5

Q1. There are 5 fish and 8 chips.
Q2. 'fewer' should be circled.
Q3.

Q4. a and c should be ticked.

PAGE 6

Q1.
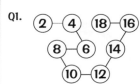
Q2. a) (5)
b) 10
c) 18
d) 21
Q3. a) (4)
b) 8
c) 22
d) 47
Q4. a) (6), (8)
b) 12, 14
c) 19, 21
d) 22, 24
e) 23, 25
f) 28, 30

PAGE 7

Q1. a) (5)
b) 9
c) 14
d) 5
e) 19
f) 13
Q2. a) 17
b) 21
c) 28
Q3. (3), 5, 7, 9, 11, 13, 16, 18
Q4. (20), 19, 15, 12, 10, 8, 6, 2

PAGE 8

Q1.

2nd   3rd   1st   4th
Q2.
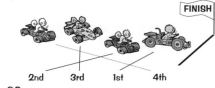
5th
Q3.

PAGE 9

Q1. a) 6
b) 10
Q2. a) (7)
b) 9
c) 6
d) 8
e) 8
f) 9
Q3. (0), (7)
e.g. 1, 6
e.g. 2, 5
e.g. 3, 4

PAGE 10

Q1.
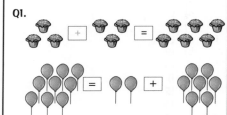
Q2. (5 + 15), 10 + 10 and 8 + 12
should all be circled.
Q3.
14 15 16 17 18 19 20 21 22 (23) 24

PAGE 11

Q1. a) (=)
b) +
c) +
d) =
e) =
f) +
Q2. a) (6)
b) 7
c) 7
d) 14
e) 5
f) 14
Q3. a) (17)
b) 19
c) 18
d) 17
e) 18
f) 17

Answers — Pages 12 to 20

PAGE 12

Q1.   2
      6
Q2.   2
Q3. a) (3)
    b) 3
    c) 5
    d) 11
    e) 11
    f) 14
    g) 13

PAGE 13

Q1. a) (10)
    b) 16
    c) 0
    d) 7
Q2. a) (12)
    b) 12
    c) 15
    d) 11
    e) 12
    f) 14
Q3. a) (7)
    b) 6
    c) 3
    d) 2
    e) 2
    f) 4

PAGE 14

Q1. a) (4)
    b) 4
    c) 6
Q2. a)

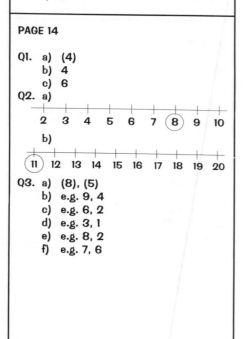

    b)

Q3. a) (8), (5)
    b) e.g. 9, 4
    c) e.g. 6, 2
    d) e.g. 3, 1
    e) e.g. 8, 2
    f) e.g. 7, 6

PAGE 15

Q1. a)

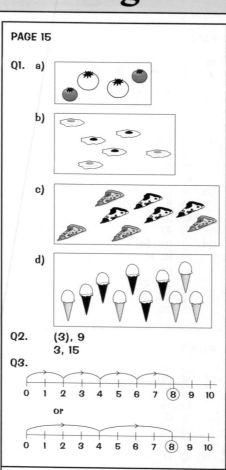

    b)

    c)

    d)

Q2.   (3), 9
      3, 15
Q3.

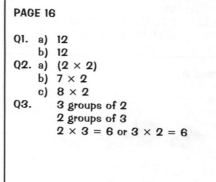

      or

PAGE 16

Q1. a) 12
    b) 12
Q2. a) (2×2)
    b) 7×2
    c) 8×2
Q3.   3 groups of 2
      2 groups of 3
      $2 \times 3 = 6$ or $3 \times 2 = 6$

PAGE 17

Q1. a)

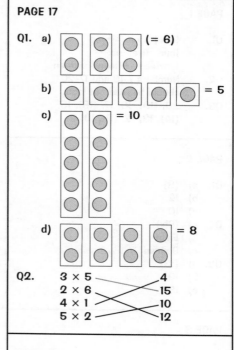

(= 6)

    b) = 5
    c) = 10
    d) = 8

Q2. 3×5 4
      2×6 15
      4×1 10
      5×2 12

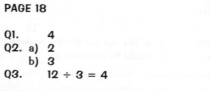

PAGE 18

Q1.   4
Q2. a) 2
    b) 3
Q3. $12 \div 3 = 4$

PAGE 19

Q1.   3
Q2.

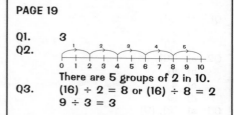

      There are 5 groups of 2 in 10.
Q3. $(16) \div 2 = 8$ or $(16) \div 8 = 2$
      $9 \div 3 = 3$

PAGE 20

Q1. a) (1)
    b) 5
    c) 3
    d) 7
Q2.

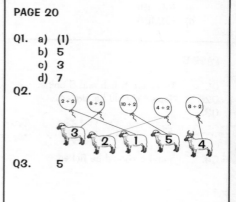

Q3.   5

Answers — Pages 21 to 29

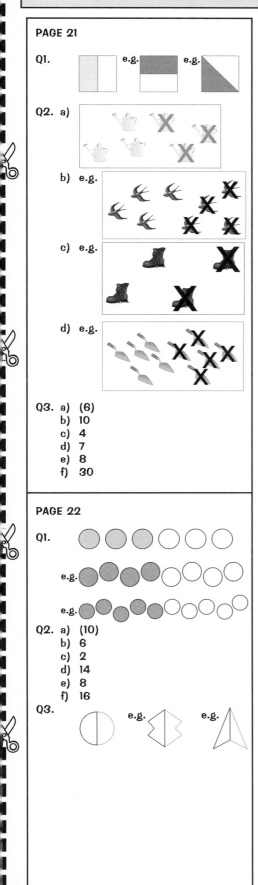

PAGE 21

Q1. [diagram]

Q2. a) [watering cans with X marks]

b) e.g. [birds with X marks]

c) e.g. [boots with X marks]

d) e.g. [trowels with X marks]

Q3. a) (6)
b) 10
c) 4
d) 7
e) 8
f) 30

PAGE 22

Q1. [circles — rows shaded]

e.g.

e.g.

Q2. a) (10)
b) 6
c) 2
d) 14
e) 8
f) 16

Q3. e.g. e.g. [shapes divided]

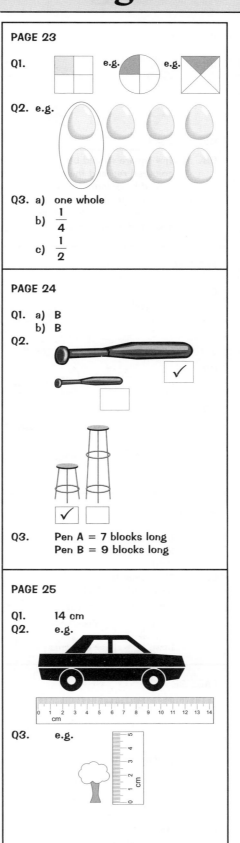

PAGE 23

Q1. [diagram] e.g. e.g.

Q2. e.g. [eggs]

Q3. a) one whole
b) $\frac{1}{4}$
c) $\frac{1}{2}$

PAGE 24

Q1. a) B
b) B

Q2. [bats — tick on larger]

[stools — tick on shorter]

Q3. Pen A = 7 blocks long
Pen B = 9 blocks long

PAGE 25

Q1. 14 cm
Q2. e.g. [car and ruler]

Q3. e.g. [tree and ruler]

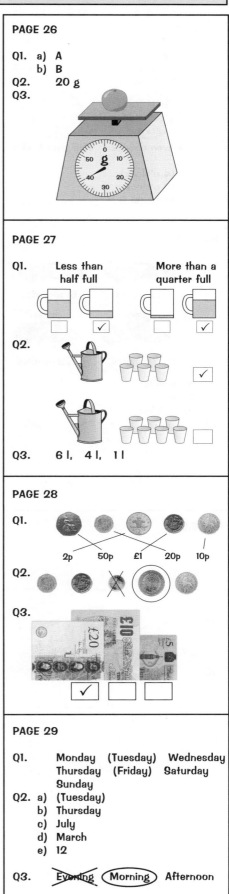

PAGE 26

Q1. a) A
b) B
Q2. 20 g
Q3. [weighing scale]

PAGE 27

Q1. Less than   More than a
half full   quarter full

[mugs with ticks]

Q2. [watering can and cups — tick]

Q3. 6 l, 4 l, 1 l

PAGE 28

Q1. [coins with crossing lines]
2p   50p   £1   20p   10p

Q2. [coins — one crossed, one circled]

Q3. [banknotes £10, £20, £5 — tick on first]

PAGE 29

Q1. Monday (Tuesday) Wednesday
Thursday (Friday) Saturday
Sunday
Q2. a) (Tuesday)
b) Thursday
c) July
d) March
e) 12

Q3. ~~Evening~~ (Morning) Afternoon

40

PAGE 30

Q1. a) (3 o'clock)
b) 6 o'clock
c) Half past 9

Q2.

Eleven o'clock   Half past twelve

Q3. (4 o'clock)
10 o'clock
Half past 6

PAGE 31

Q1. a)

15 seconds   51 seconds

b)

3 minutes   23 minutes

Q2. a) slower
b) quicker
c) quicker

Q3.

PAGE 32

Q1.

square   triangle   circle

Q2.

Q3. e.g.

PAGE 33

Q1.

Q2. e.g.

Q3. a) The square should be coloured red and the circles should be coloured blue.
b) The triangle should be coloured red and the squares should be coloured blue.

PAGE 34

Q1.

sphere   cube   pyramid

Q2.

red   blue

Q3.

PAGE 35

Q1. between
left
right

Q2. The computer is on top of the desk.
The books are underneath the desk.

Q3. Up ☐   Backwards ✓

Down ☐   Forwards ☐

PAGE 36

Q1.

Q2. Three-quarter turn clockwise should be ticked.

Q3. 9

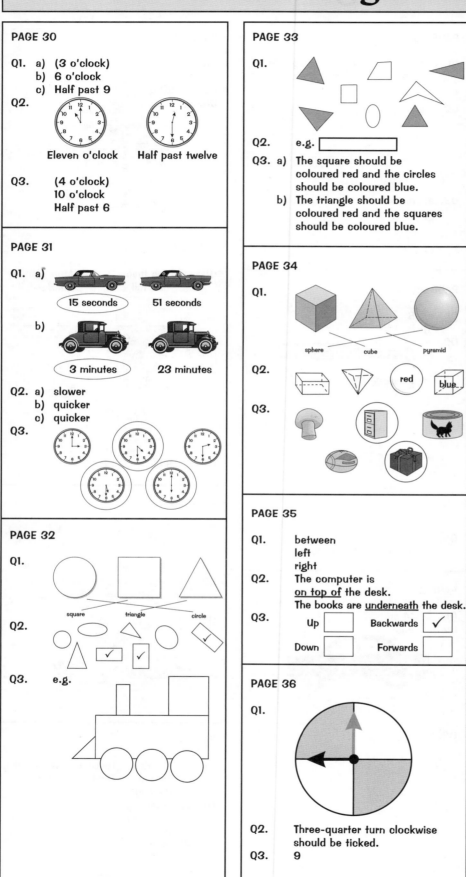

M1W11